My Teddy Bear Story Book

Illustration © Anthony Fletcher 1993.
Text and compilation © Irwin Jorvik Ltd 1993.

The right of Anthony Fletcher to be identified as the author of the
illustration has been asserted pursuant to ss 77 and 78 of the act.

Kibworth Books,
Imperial Road,
Kibworth Beauchamp,
England.

I.S.B.N. 0-7239-0092-9

Typesetting by C.A.T.S. Ltd., Leeds.

Printed and Bound in Italy.

MY TEDDY BEAR

AT PLAY

Teddy Bear and his friends the toys are in the backyard. The sun is shining. Teddy Bear and Toy Soldier are playing catch with a shiny red ball. Back and forth, they throw the ball, high up in the air. Toy Soldier throws it so high that he doesn't see the fat cat behind him, and he trips over his tail!

Rag Doll and Clown are sitting on the swing.

They are playing a game of 'I spy'.

Clown has to find a word beginning with the letter 's'. Could it be snail, or spade? 'No, that's not the word,' says Rag Doll. 'The right word is shoe.' Teddy has found something beginning with the letter 's' as well.

All of the toys enjoy taking it in turns to jump over a rope. Rag Rabbit and Wooden Doll are turning the rope for Teddy Bear. Rag Rabbit is very small and he can't get the rope high enough. Teddy has caught his leg in the rope and has fallen into the flowers. 'Are you alright, Teddy?' asks his friend the Clown.

It's started to rain. The sky is very dark, and it looks like it is going to last for quite a long time. The toys are hurrying indoors. Teddy Bear is helping Wooden Duck and Rag Rabbit. They can't run as fast as the others. They are all getting soaked through, and they are very miserable because the rain has spoiled all the fun they were having.

Indoors it is nice and dry. The toys have

decided to play hide-and-seek, and they have

chosen Teddy to be 'It'. Teddy has to count to

twenty, and then he has to search every room

in the house until he finds them. Teddy doesn't

mind being the one who has to search. His

friends are not very good at hiding, and it is

always easy to find them.

After hide-and-seek, Rag Doll teaches Teddy

and Clown how to make a jigsaw puzzle. It is

very easy. Rag Doll has found a nice picture of

a car in an old magazine. She has glued the

picture onto a piece of cardboard, and now

she is cutting the cardboard into lots of

different shapes that Teddy and Clown can

make up into a picture again.

Rag Elephant would rather ride in a car than make jigsaw puzzles out of pictures of them. He has found some old boxes, and he has painted wheels, headlamps, and a license plate onto them. He could not find anything to use as a steering wheel, so he is using an old cushion. Rag Rabbit is just putting the finishing touches to the hood, and of they'll go!

Teddy and Rag Doll like to play with building blocks. Teddy is building a wall with square blocks, and Rag Doll is building a tall tower out of lots of different shapes. Rag Doll has to stand on the tip of her toes to reach up high enough. She has to keep her hand very still so that the last block will balance on the top.

All of the toys like to play blindman's bluff. It is

Clown's turn to wear the spotted blindfold.

They are all running around Clown and

teasing him, because they know he is not very

good at this game. Rag Rabbit has just thrown

a balloon to Clown. Poor Clown thinks he has

caught Teddy by the ears! The toys think this

game is great fun.

The toys are too tired to play any more. They sit down in front of the fire. Soon it will be supper time. They spend a little while looking at favorite picture books. 'Hooray!' cries Toy Soldier, 'The sun is beginning to come out again.' Sure enough, the rain begins to stop, and through the window, the toys can soon see a lovely rainbow, as the sun comes back out again.

MY TEDDY BEAR

AT WORK

Teddy Bear and Clown are reading a newspaper. Clown has found a story about a fireman. There is a picture of him in uniform standing next to his fire engine. Clown would like to be a fireman too. Teddy makes a list of all his favorite jobs. 'I will just have to try them all,' he says.

Teddy would like to work in an office. He could write important letters on a typewriter.

There is a lot to do, sticking stamps on envelopes, and then sealing them up for the mail. He is much too busy to keep his desk tidy. Teddy is a messy worker.

'Perhaps I would make a good doctor,' says

Teddy. He wears a special white coat, and

carries a funny instrument called a

stethoscope. Teddy gets lots of practice

bandaging Wooden Doll's hand. He has

already put Toy Soldier's arm in a sling after

he was hurt in a make-believe battle!

This is Teddy Bear's shop. He has a pair of

scales to weigh fruit and vegetables. Rag Doll

is buying some of the fruit that Teddy has just

weighed. She wants an orange and a banana

for her lunch. Teddy will put them in a bag

while Rag Doll finds two coins, one for each

kind of fruit.

Teddy Bear likes to play the piano. He is giving a concert to some of his friends. He looks very smart in his white tie, and black tail-coat. His friend Toy Soldier plays a musical instrument too. He beats his drum in time to the music.

Now Teddy is a circus star. Rag Rabbit and

Clown are pretending to be his 'lions'. He has

borrowed Rag Doll's whip and top so that he

can make a cracking noise just like they used

to do in the circus. Teddy likes wearing the

shining uniform, with its brass buttons and hat.

Being a teacher is fun. Teddy Bear draws on a blackboard. He is showing the toys how to do their math. They are learning how to add up.

Rag Doll thinks addition is very easy, and she has already finished. The others are finding it much harder. They haven't even started.

Teddy Bear has made his blackboard into an easel, so that he can paint a picture. An artist mixes paints together, and sloshes them onto paper. Teddy likes being an artist because it is a messy job. He likes to paint, and today he has painted a picture of himself in the garden.

Trying all these different jobs is hungry work for a little bear, so Teddy decides he'd like to be a chef. He wears a tall white hat and an apron. Teddy is going to make vegetable soup, but he isn't a very good cook. He doesn't realize that he has to cut the vegetables up before they go into the pan!

Now Teddy Bear has tried all the jobs he listed

in his notebook. He is really not sure which

job he likes best. Wooden Doll has brought

Teddy his favorite meal, a glass of milk and

bread with strawberry jam. 'Perhaps I will just

be a stay-at-home bear,' he says,

sipping his milk.

MY TEDDY BEAR

AT HOME

Teddy Bear is waiting for his friends to arrive.

They have promised to come and visit today.

Teddy hopes that they remember that it is a

rather important day for a little bear. He is

very excited, perhaps he will even get some

presents.

But first Teddy must tidy his room. His clothes

are scattered all over the floor. One by one, he

picks them up and puts them in the closet.

Oh dear, Teddy Bear has lost his socks.

"There they are behind the clock," laughs his

friend the Clown, who has just arrived with

Little Wooden Duck. "Can we help?,"

they ask.

Little Wooden Duck helps Rag Rabbit make Teddy Bear's bed. He has found some clean sheets and a blanket in the cupboard. Making the bed is very hard work. At last it is done, except there is a funny bump right in the middle! What is it? Wooden Duck suddenly remembers, they have left the pillow under the sheets and will have to start all over again!

Wooden Doll is downstairs sweeping the floor with a broom. There are lots of crumbs under the table where she finds Teddy Bear's watch. He is always losing his things. Though he is very pleased that she has found it, he is also beginning to feel disappointed. Nobody has remembered that today is a special day.

At last his friends have helped him tidy up the house. Picking up a dustcloth he begins to polish the mirror and dust the shelves. He has to stretch up high to reach them and he nearly knocks the goldfish out of its bowl. There are lots of ornaments to dust and he thinks he will never finish.

Elephant is helping by watering a large plant.

It's very thirsty. The plant has not been

watered for a long time, so Elephant uses his

long trunk to do the job. But while all of this

activity is going on, Wooden Doll and Clown

have prepared a surprize for Teddy.

Happy Birthday Teddy! The toys have just been helping to tidy up. They all came to arrange Teddy Bear's surprize party with balloons and streamers, and a magnificent cake. Teddy Bear is so happy. His friends didn't forget after all.

There are lots of dirty dishes to wash before
the toys can play games. Teddy Bear washes
all of the bowls and spoons, and his friends
dry the dishes, ready to put away. Wooden
Doll is very busy, making sure they all do their
jobs properly.

Now that the kitchen is tidied and all the

supper things cleared away, they all go up to

the nursery. Teddy Bear rides his new rocking

horse which he has named 'Picnic'. After they

have played some games together it is time for

his friends to go home. It has been a lovely

day.

Teddy Bear enjoyed himself so much. He thought everybody had forgotten it was his birthday, it turned out to be the best ever. He got a new tennis racquet, a ball, and a shining new sailboat, as the day ended he was planning his next adventure when he and his friends would take the sailboat out to the shallow boating lake in the park.

MY TEDDY BEAR

ON VACATION

Teddy Bear and all the toys are traveling on a train to the shore. Wooden Doll is dressed in her summer clothes, and Teddy is wearing a sailor hat. It is a long journey, but there are lots of things to see outside, as the train passes through the countryside.

At last the train has arrived at the station. The toys jump down from the box car and hurry along the platform. They are in such a rush to get to the ocean they have left poor Teddy Bear to carry all the bags. 'Wait for me,' he calls.

Toy Soldier and Rag Elephant want to splash in the water. They run across the soft sand and jump in and out of the waves. Wooden Doll and Clown don't like getting wet. They are collecting seashells further up the beach. They are going to gather the shells in a basket.

Rag Rabbit and Rag Doll are sitting in a large

stripey deckchair. They are enjoying the

sunshine. It's a little bit too hot for Teddy, so

he is sitting in the shade under an umbrella.

Here come Wooden Duck and Clown. They

want Teddy to play paddle ball.

The rock pools are very interesting. The toys

can see all sorts of creatures in the water. Toy

Soldier has spotted a crab, and Teddy Bear is

trying to catch a fish to show to Clown, but

they are hiding in the seaweed, and they won't

come out.

It's time for lunch. Everybody is very hungry. It

has been a very busy morning. Teddy Bear has

packed a huge picnic basket full of food. The

toys have spread a large cloth over the sand.

Rag Doll has put lots of sandwiches and cakes

onto a plate. A friendly little dog hopes that

there will be some left for him.

Wooden Doll has found another pail at the bottom of the basket. 'Now we can build a sandcastle,' says Teddy Bear. 'We will build the biggest sandcastle on the beach, and you can decorate it with shells,' he says to Wooden Doll. Wooden Doll uses the shells that she collected with Clown.

After they build the sandcastle, Teddy decides

to try rowing a boat on a nearby boating

pond. There is a lot of food left over from

lunch, and Teddy takes this with him to feed

the ducks. He sees lots of other animals too.

There are colorful butterflies, a bright green

frog and a family of swans.

The toys are hot after digging in the sand. An ice cream will cool them down. Clown carries the ice cream back from the store, but a hungry seagull tries to steal them, and Clown drops them on the beach. They are all covered in sand. Clown will have to go back to the store to buy some more.

It's time to go home. All the toys are

exhausted as they take a short bus ride back to

the railway station. They have had a lovely

day. 'I wonder what we will see on the way

home,' says Teddy Bear to his friends, but

nobody replies. They are all fast asleep,

dreaming happily about the shore.

PLACE

A PHOTOGRAPH OF YOU

AND YOUR TEDDY

HERE